IT'S EASY TO PLAY
COLDPLAY

CW00347061

Wise Publications
part of The Music Sales Group

London / New York / Paris / Sydney / Copenhagen / Berlin / Madrid / Tokyo

Published by
Wise Publications
8/9 Frith Street, London W1D 3JB, UK.

Exclusive Distributors:
Music Sales Limited
Distribution Centre, Newmarket Road, Bury St Edmunds, Suffolk IP33 3YB, UK.
Music Sales Pty Limited
120 Rothschild Avenue, Rosebery, NSW 2018, Australia.

Order No. AM983477
ISBN 1-84609-194-2
This book © Copyright 2005 Wise Publications,
a division of Music Sales Limited.

Music arranged by Derek Jones.
Music processed by Paul Ewers Music Design.
Original Design by Tappin Gofton.
Printed in the United Kingdom by Caligraving Limited, Thetford, Norfolk.

Your Guarantee of Quality
As publishers, we strive to produce every book to the highest commercial standards.
The music has been freshly engraved and the book has been carefully designed to
minimise awkward page turns and to make playing from it a real pleasure.
Particular care has been given to specifying acid-free, neutral-sized paper made from
pulps which have not been elemental chlorine bleached.
This pulp is from farmed sustainable forests and was produced with special regard for the environment.
Throughout, the printing and binding have been planned to ensure a sturdy,
attractive publication which should give years of enjoyment.
If your copy fails to meet our high standards, please inform us and we will gladly replace it.

www.musicsales.com

Square One

Words & Music by Guy Berryman, Jon Buckland, Will Champion & Chris Martin

1. You're in con-trol, is there a - ny - where you want to go?

You're in con-trol, is there a - ny - thing you want to know?

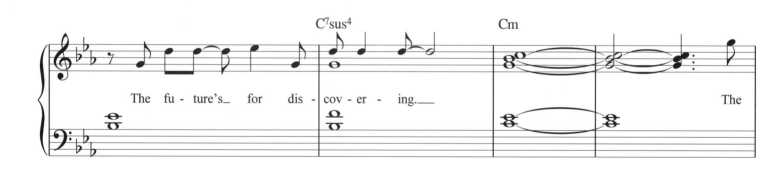

The fu - ture's_ for dis - cov - er - ing. The

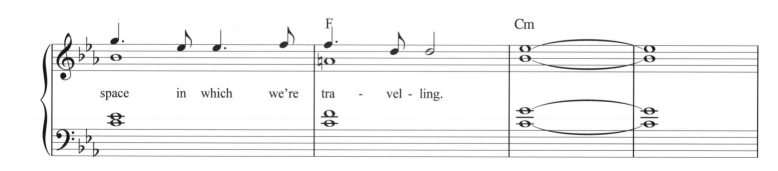

space in which we're tra - vel - ling.

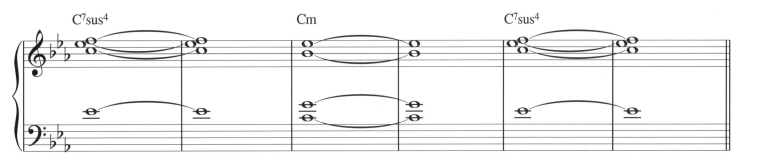

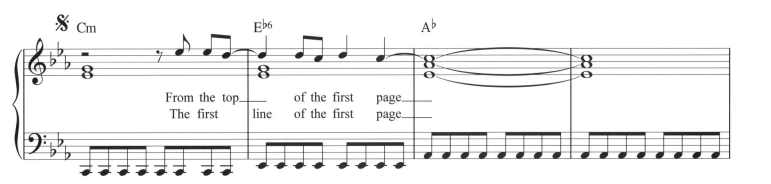

From the top of the first page
The first line of the first page

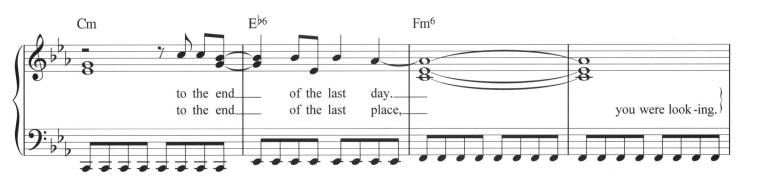

to the end of the last day.
to the end of the last place, you were look-ing.

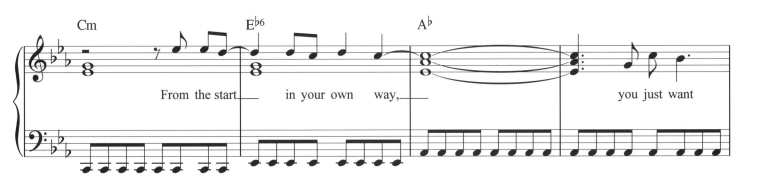

From the start in your own way, you just want

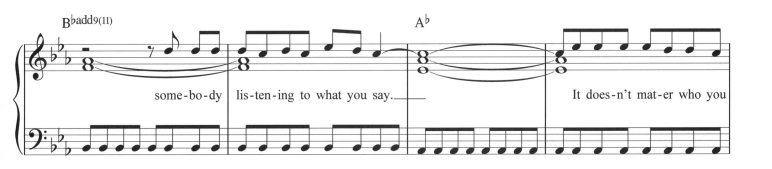

some-bo-dy lis-ten-ing to what you say. It does-n't mat-er who you

there who is lost and hurt and lone-ly too? Are they bleed-ing all your col-ours in-to one? And if you come un-done as if you'd been run through, some ca-ta-pult had fired you. You won-der if your chance-'ll ev-er come or if you're stuck in square one.

9

What If

Words & Music by Guy Berryman, Jon Buckland, Will Champion & Chris Martin

1. What if there was no light, no-thing wrong, no-thing right?

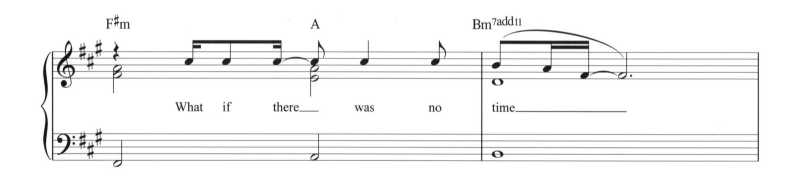

What if there was no time and no rea-son or rhyme?

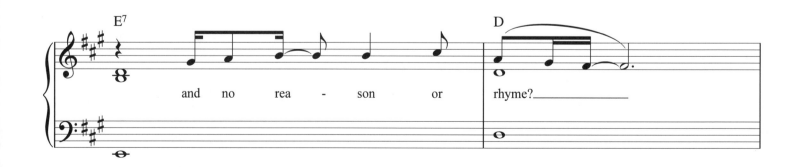

What if you___ should de - cide___ that you

don't want me there by your side, that you

don't want me there in your life?

2. What if I___ got it wrong___ and no po - em or

3. Ev - 'ry step_ that you take___ could be your_ big - gest mis-

song___ could put right_ what I got wrong___

take.___ It could bend_ or it could break,___

11

13

White Shadows

Words & Music by Guy Berryman, Jon Buckland, Will Champion & Chris Martin

1. When I was a young boy__ I tried to__
2. If you ev - er feel like__ some - thing's__
3. When I was a young boy__ I tried to__

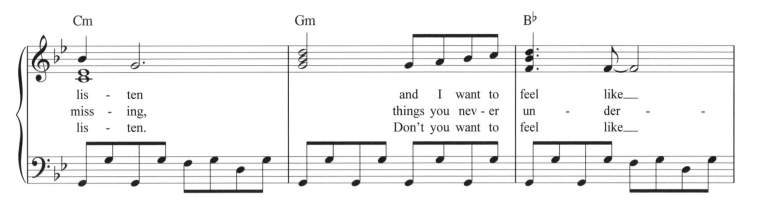

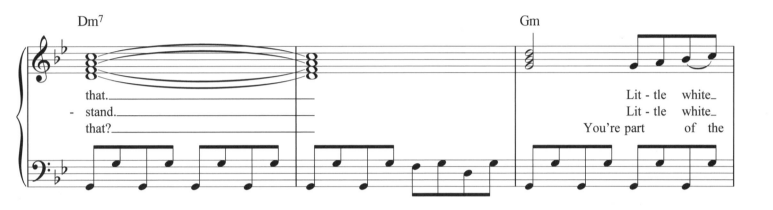

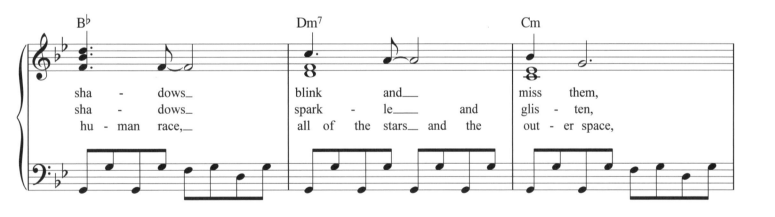

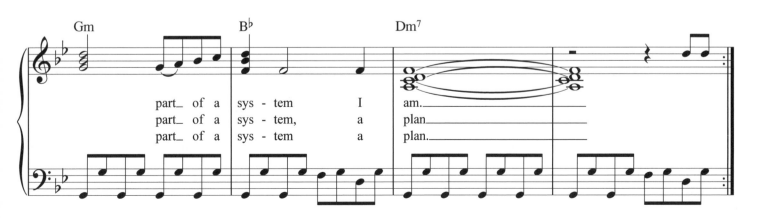

Swim out on a sea of fa - ces,   the tide of the
See it in the new sun - rise and see it break - ing on

hu - man ra - ces.   Oh, an an - swer now   is what I
your ho - ri - zon.   Oh, an come on love,   stay with

need.
me.

Talk

Words & Music by Guy Berryman, Jon Buckland, Will Champion, Chris Martin,

Karl Bartos, Ralf Huetter & Emil Schult

Oh, bro-ther I can't____ be-lieve it's true.

I'm so scared a-bout the fu-ture and__ I want____ to talk to you.__

Oh, I want__ to talk to you.____

You could

take a pic-ture of some-thing you see.__

3° don't know where you're go-ing and you want to talk.__

20

Fix You

Words & Music by Guy Berryman, Jon Buckland, Will Champion & Chris Martin

X&Y

Words & Music by Guy Berryman, Jon Buckland, Will Champion & Chris Martin

You and me are float - ing on a ti - dal wave___

to - geth - er. You and me are drift - ing in - to out - er space___

and sing - ing.___ Ooh.___

Ooh.___

30

You and me are float - ing on a ti - dal wave____ to-geth-er.

You and me are drift - ing in-to out - er space____

and sing - ing.____ Ooh.____ Ooh.

Speed Of Sound

Words & Music by Guy Berryman, Jon Buckland, Will Champion & Chris Martin

34

35

A Message

Words & Music by Guy Berryman, Jon Buckland, Will Champion & Chris Martin

38

40

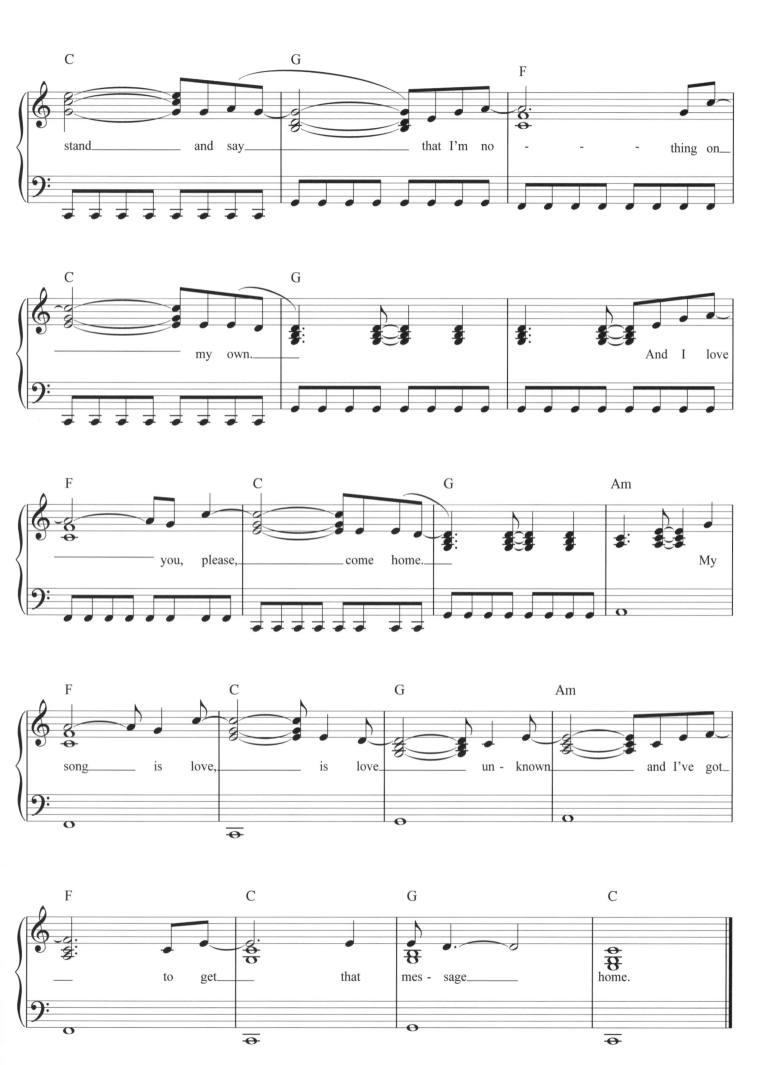

Low

Words & Music by Guy Berryman, Jon Buckland, Will Champion & Chris Martin

43

44

Coda I

C

Asus⁴

You should try.

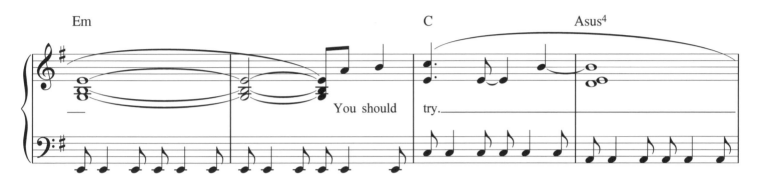

Em

C

Asus⁴

You should try.

Em

D.S.S. al Coda II

Coda II

C

Don't you wan - na see it_____ come
Don't you wan - na see it_____ come

Asus⁴

Em

soon, float - ing in a big white_____ bal - loon, or giv - en on your
down? There for throw - ing your arms_____ a - round and say "You're not a

Swallowed In The Sea

Words & Music by Guy Berryman, Jon Buckland, Will Champion & Chris Martin

48

The Hardest Part

Words & Music by Guy Berryman, Jon Buckland, Will Champion & Chris Martin

Twisted Logic

Words & Music by Guy Berryman, Jon Buckland, Will Champion & Chris Martin.

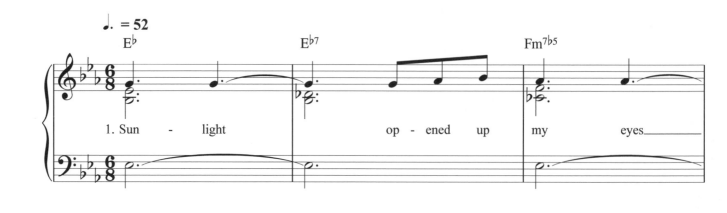

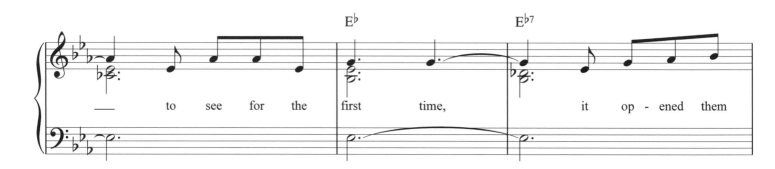

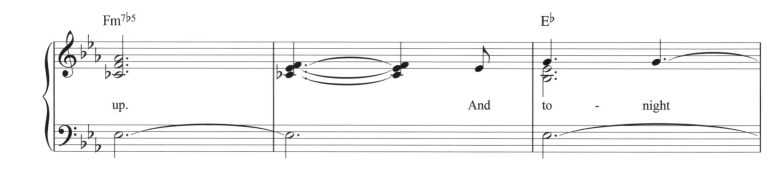

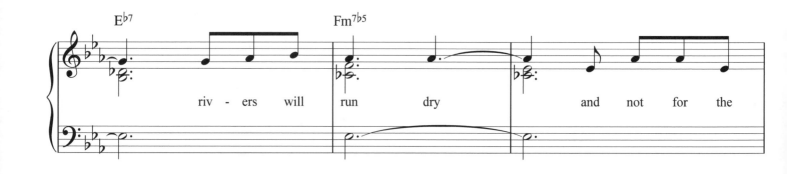

first time   riv - ers will   run.

2. Hun - dreds   of years in the   fu -   ture
(3.) - at - ed,   then drilled and   in - va -   ded.

there could be com - pu -   ters   look - ing for
If some - bo - dy   made   it,   some - one will

life
mess_____

on
it

earth.
up.

Don't fight for the
And you are not

wrong
wrong

side,
to

say what you
ask who does this be -

feel
-long

like,
to?

say how you
It be - longs to

feel.
all

of us.___

To Coda ⊕

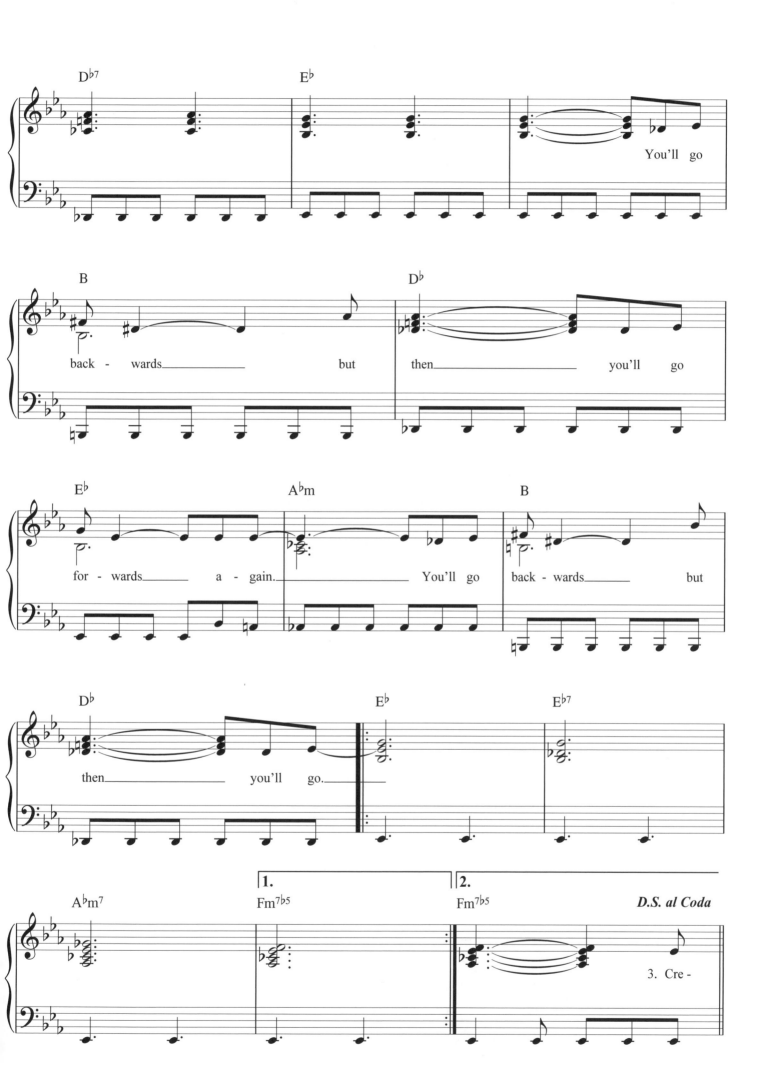

Til Kingdom Come

Words & Music by Guy Berryman, Jon Buckland, Will Champion & Chris Martin

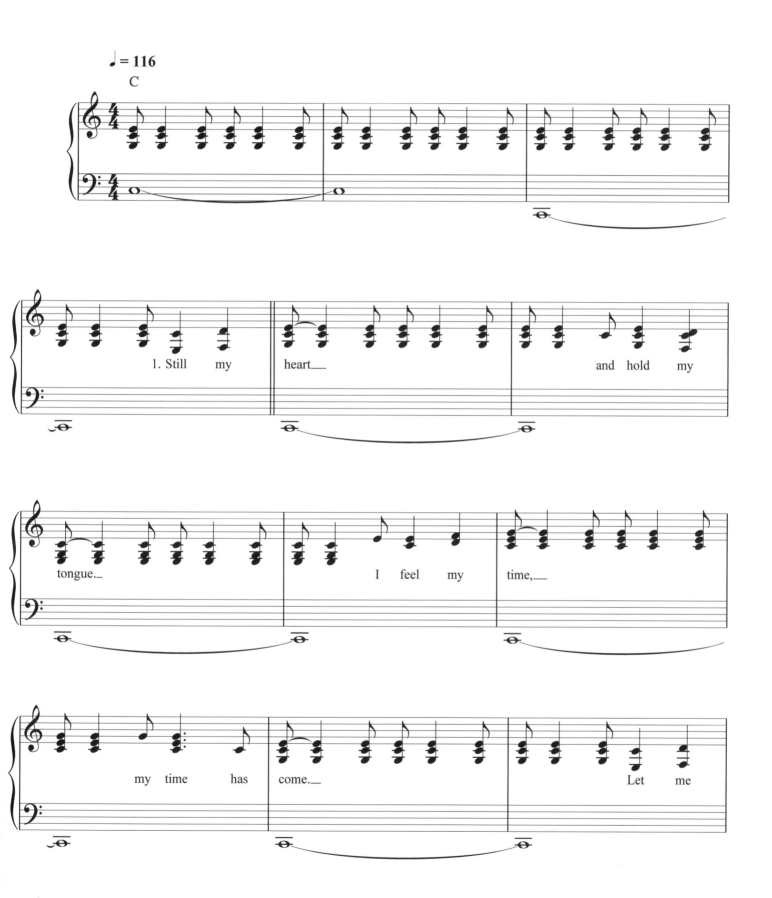

63

3/06(58018)